Things Moms Say

A Funny Coloring Book for Mama

@papeteriebleu

Papeterie Bleu

Shop our other books at
www.pbleu.com

For questions and customer service, email us at
support@pbleu.com

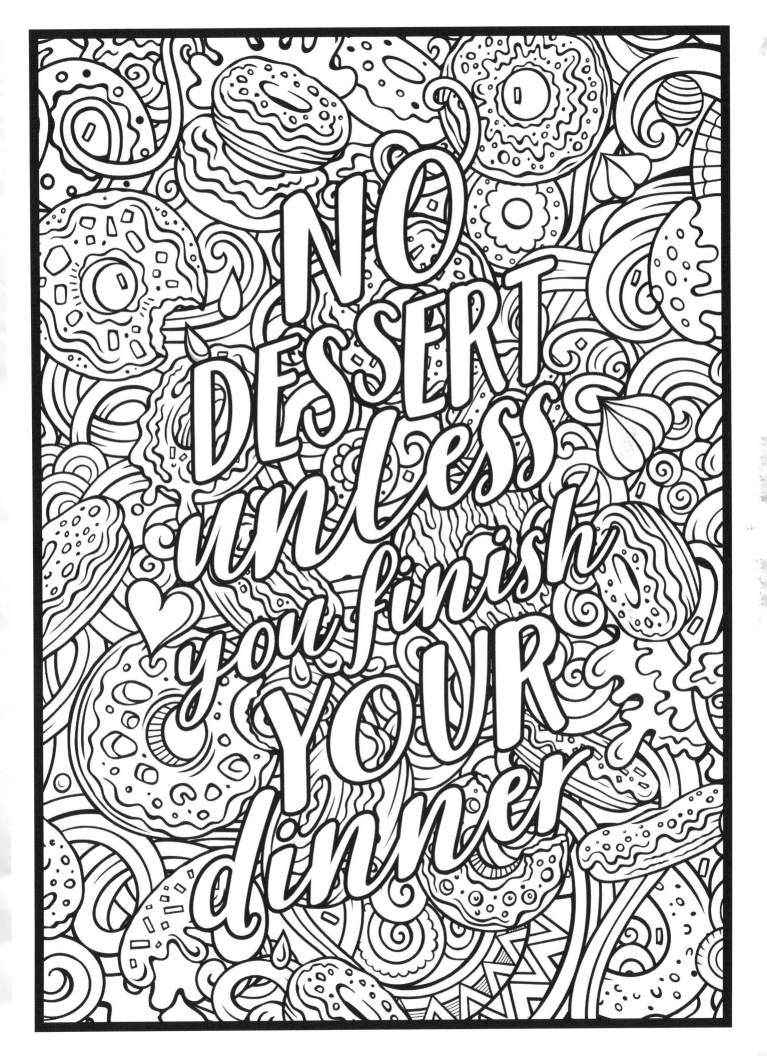

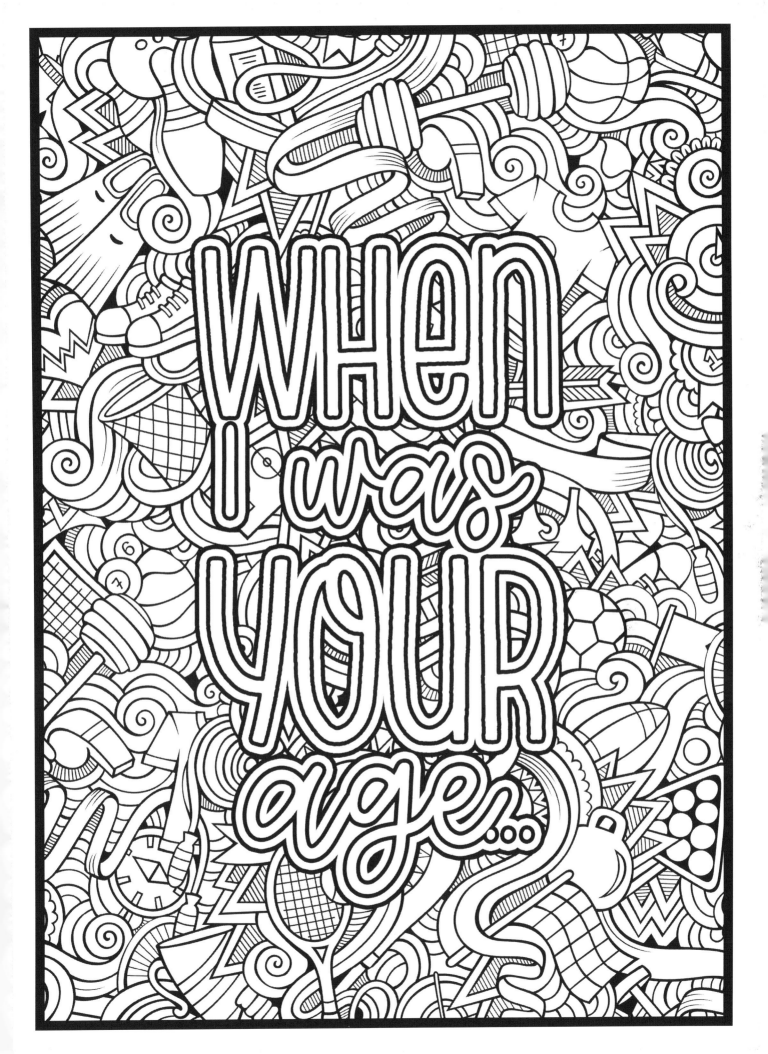

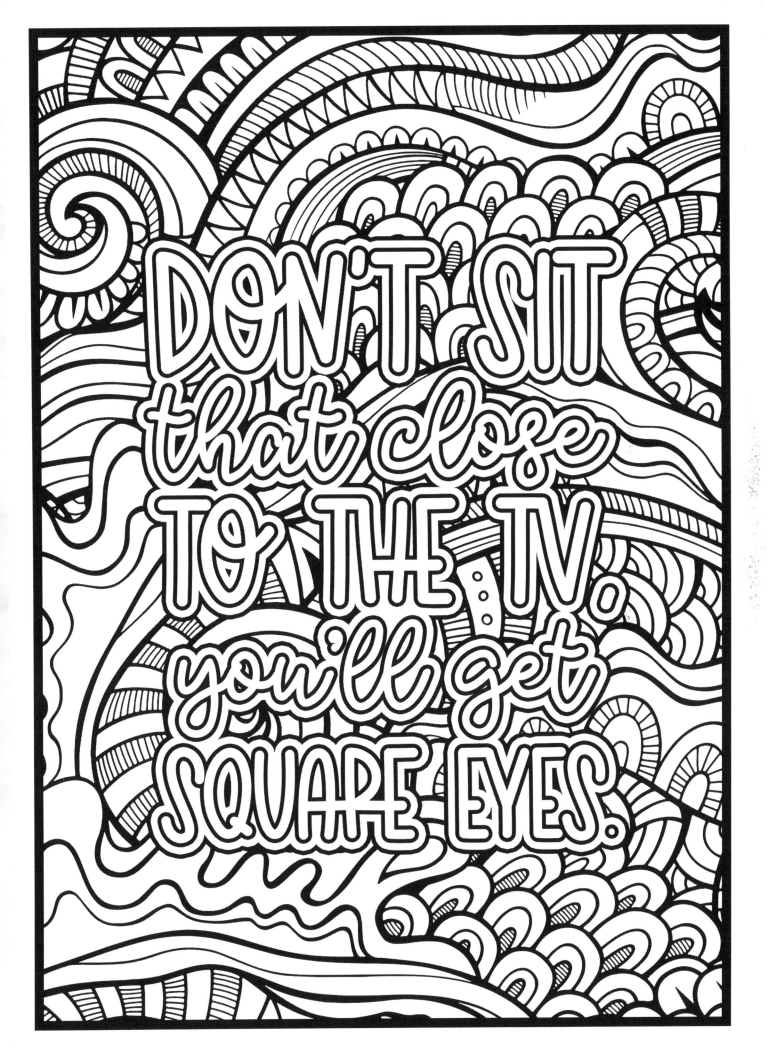

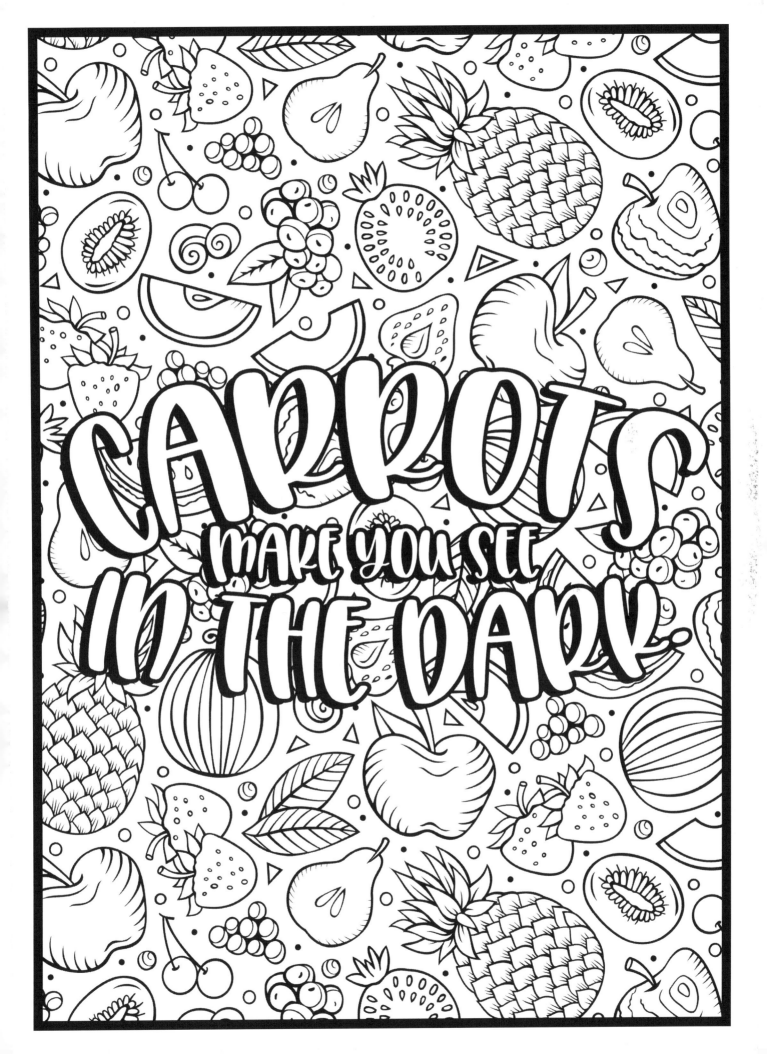

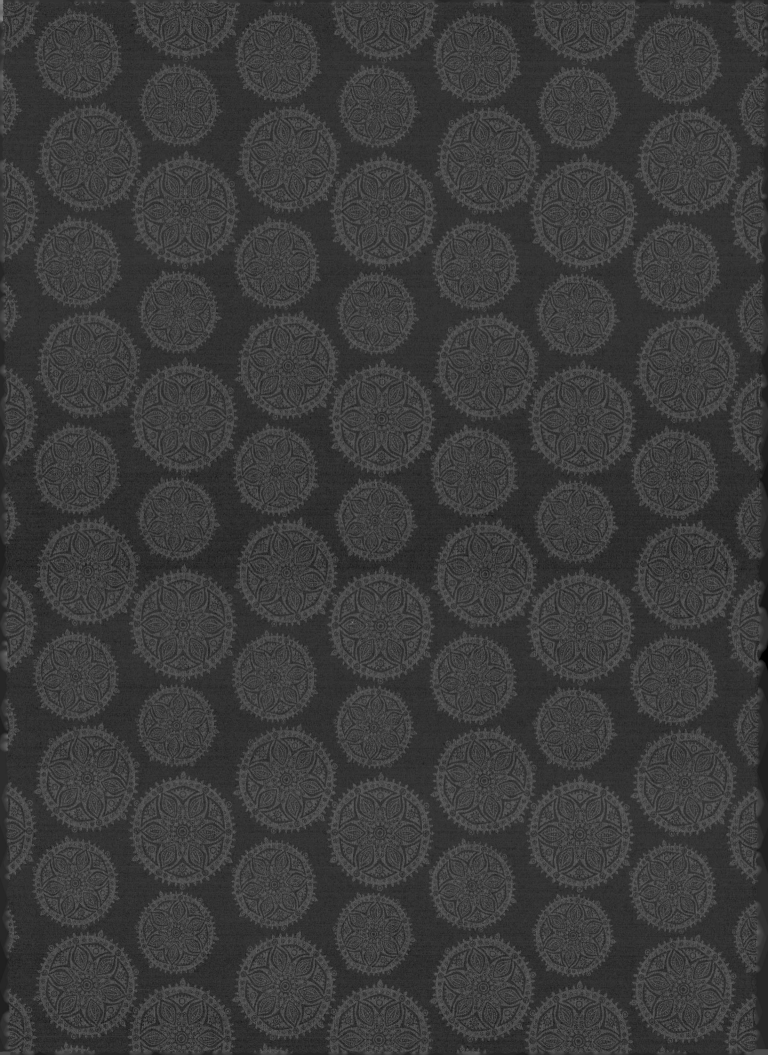

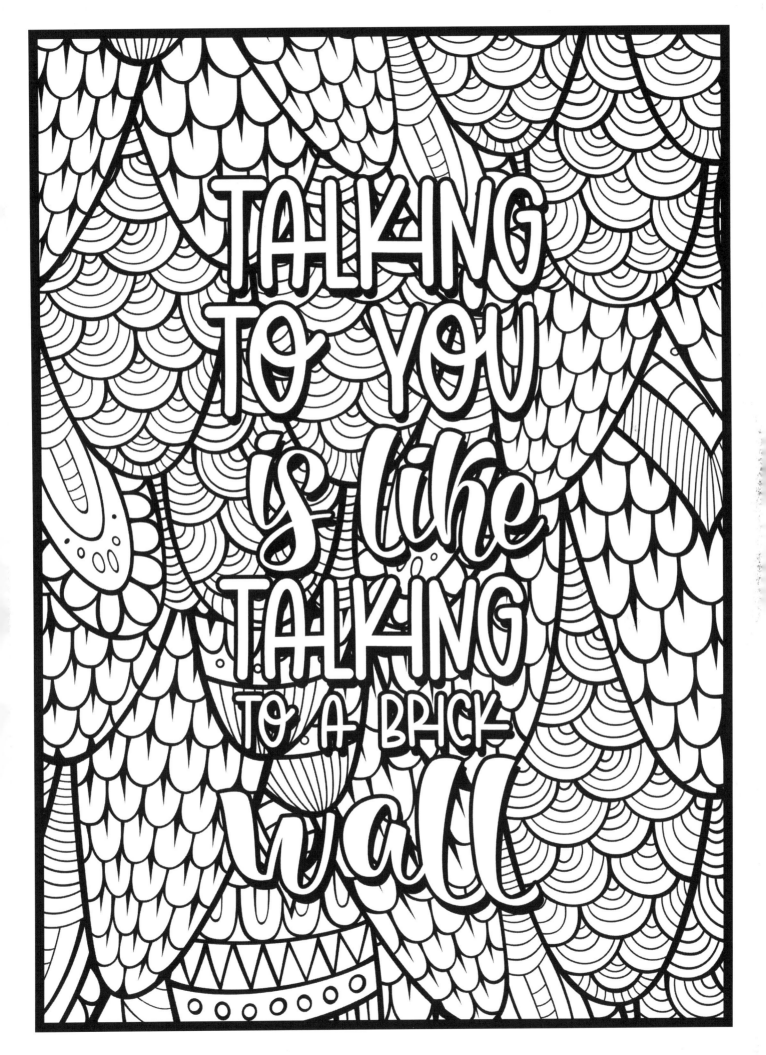

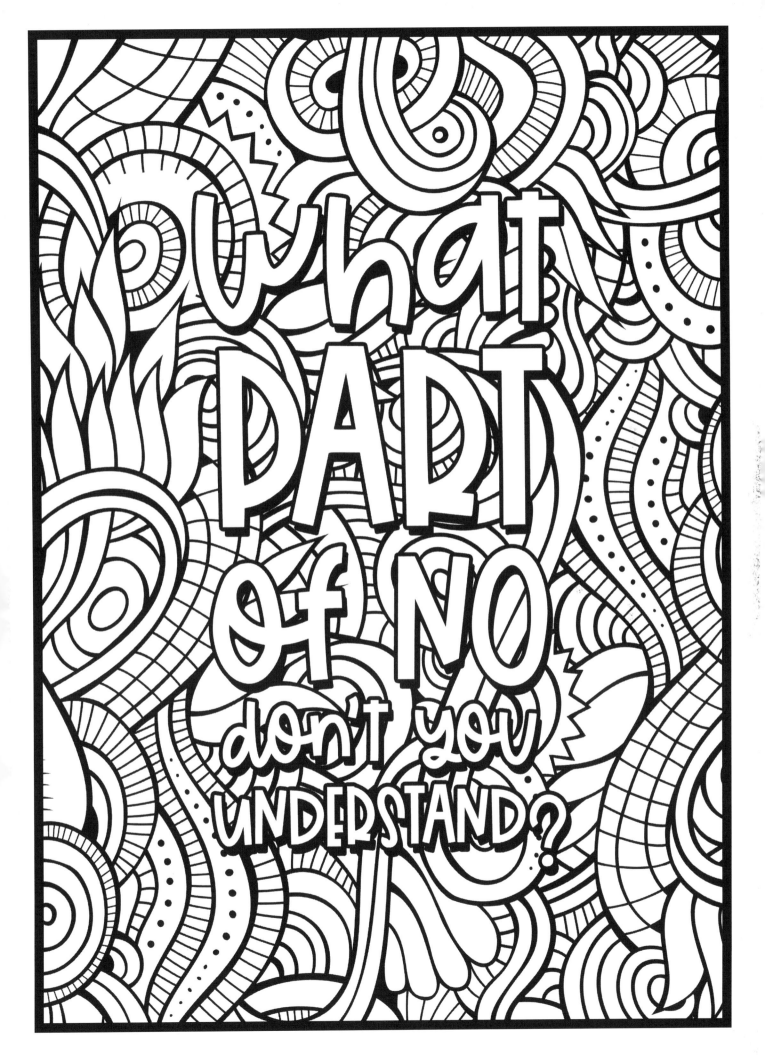

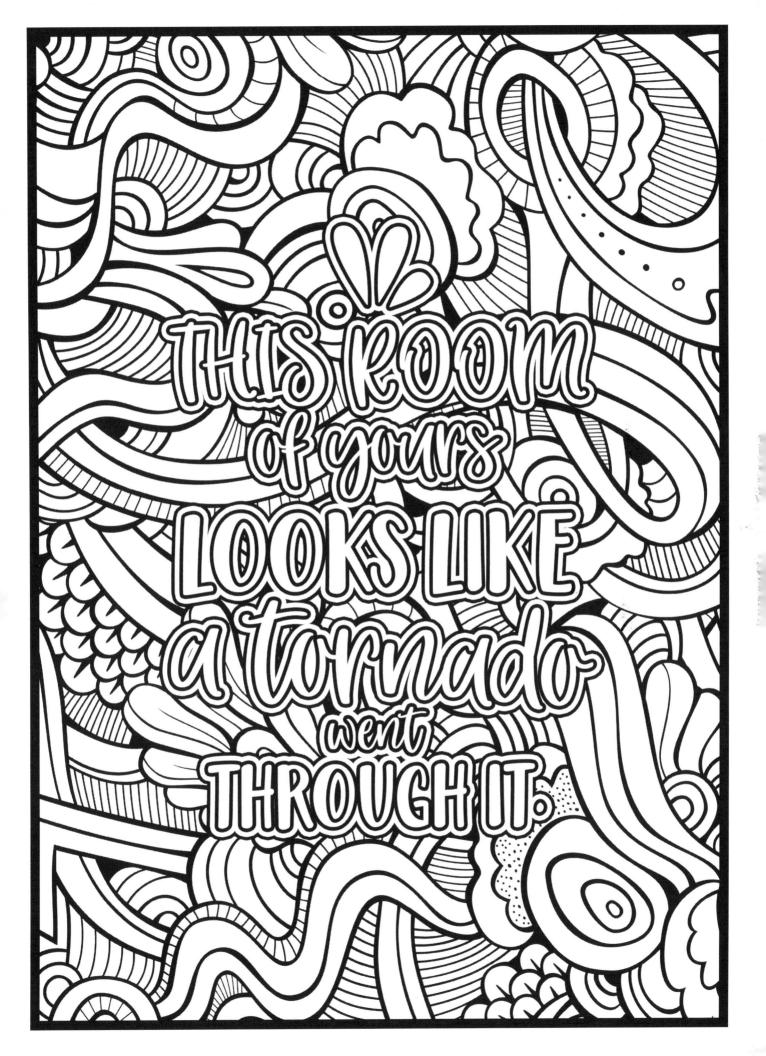

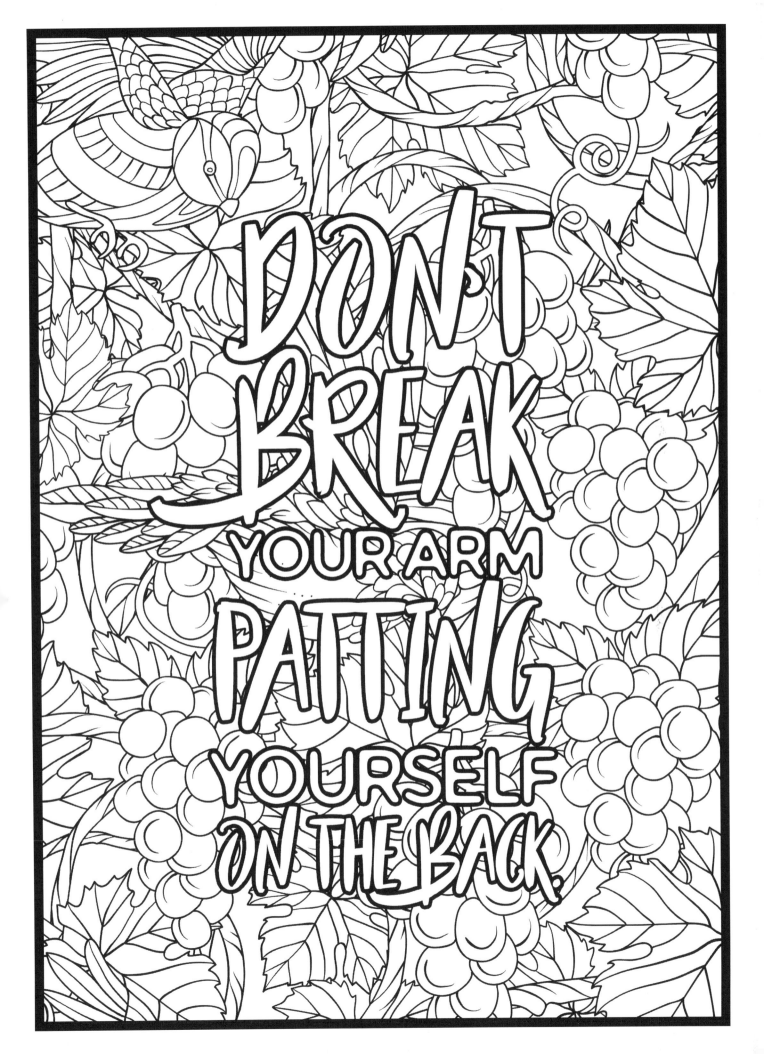

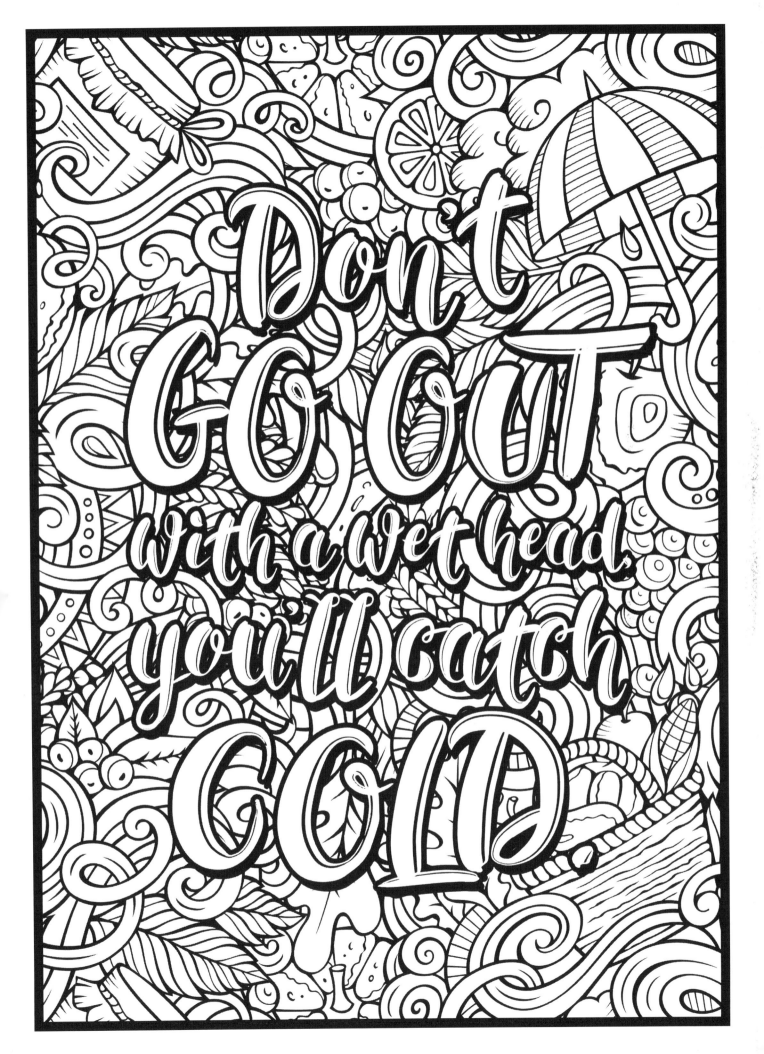

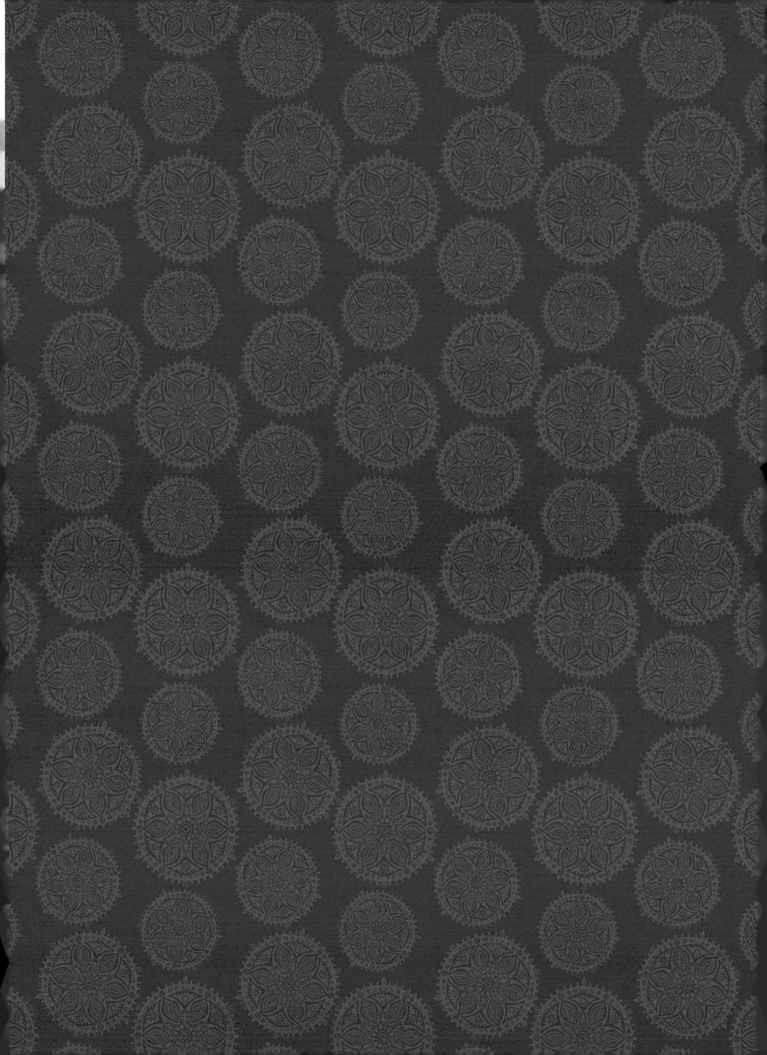

When you have YOUR OWN HOUSE then you can make THE RULES!

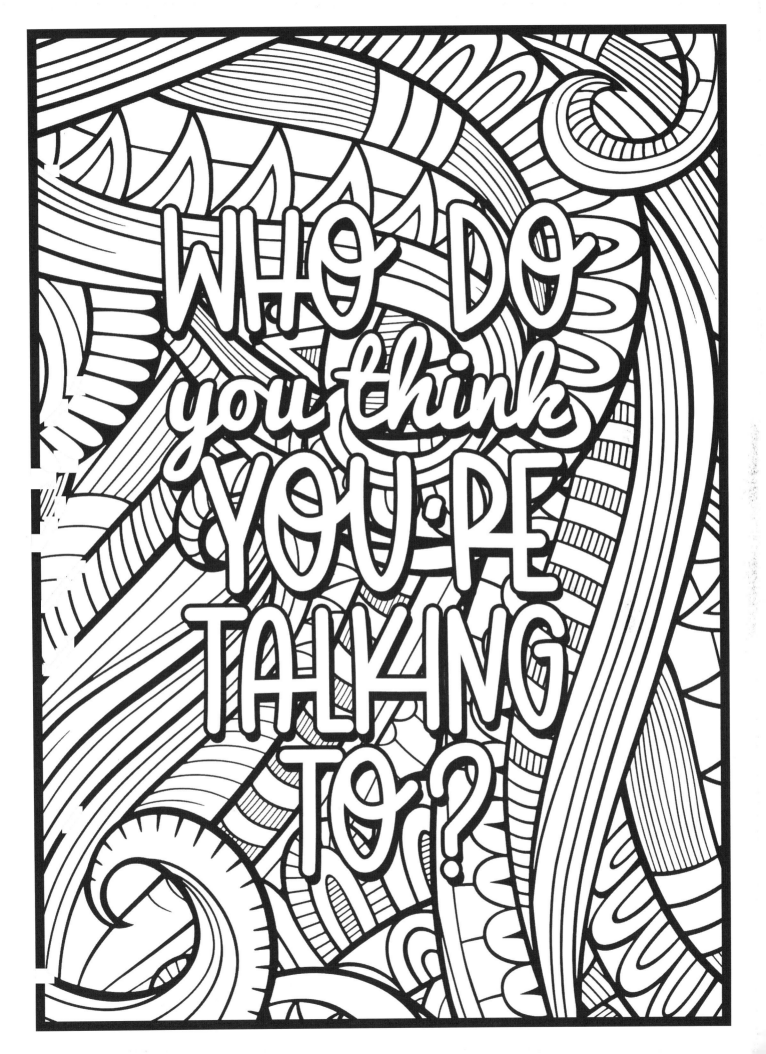

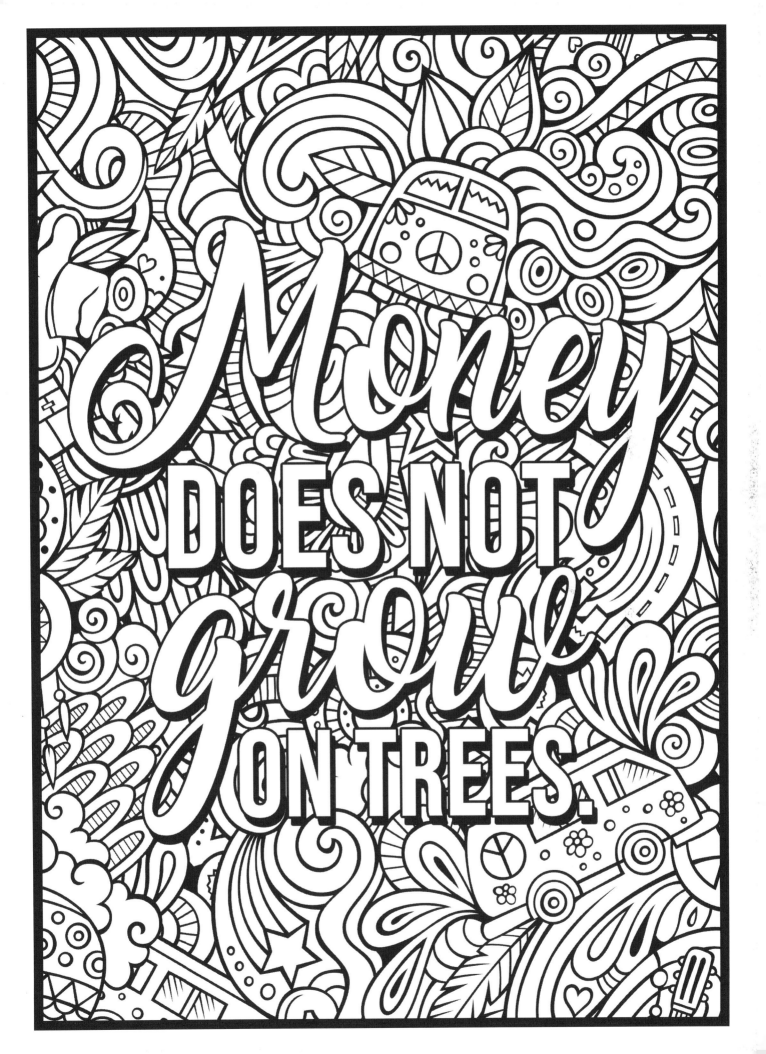

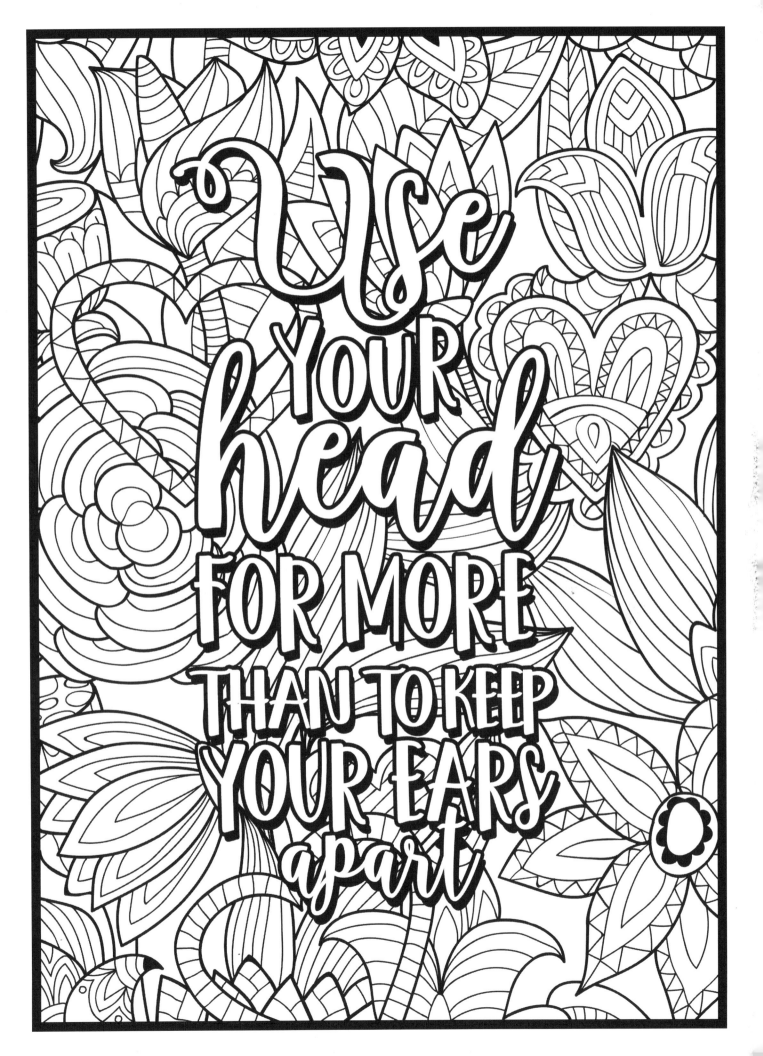

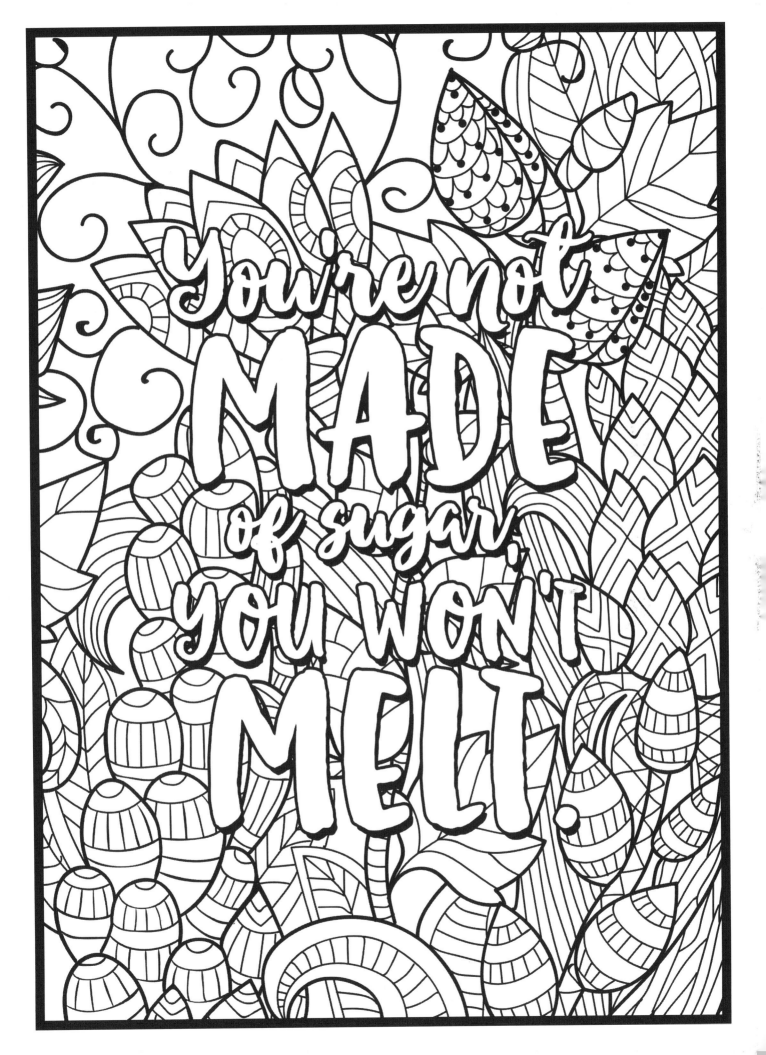

@papeteriebleu

Papeterie Bleu

Made in the USA
Middletown, DE
10 March 2022